GEORDIE SONGS, JOKES & RECITATIONS

First published by Frank Graham
Published by Butler Publishing in 1986
Revised 1998

ISBN 0 946928 47 9

BUTLER *publishing*

Thropton, Morpeth, Northumberland, NE65 7LP

The Blaydon Races

Aw went to Blaydon Races,
   'twas on the ninth of Joon,
Eiteen hundred an' sixty two,
   on a summer's efternoon,
Aw tuek the bus frae Balmbra's,
   an' she wis heavy laden,
Away we went alang Collingwood Street,
   that's on the road to Blaydon.

Chorus:
O lads, ye shud a' seen us gannin,
We passed the foakes upon the road just as they wor stannin;
Thor wes lots o' lads an' lasses there, all wi' smiling faces,
Gan alang the Scotswood Road, to see the Blaydon Races.

We flew past Armstrong's factory, and up to the "Robin Adair",
Just gan doon te the railway bridge, the bus wheel flew off there,
The lasses lost their crinolines off, an' the veils that hide their faces.
An' aw got two black eyes an' a broken nose in gan te Blaydon Races.

 Chorus - *O lads, etc.*

When we gat the wheel put on away we went agyen,
But them that had their noses broke, they cam' back ower hyem.
Sum went to the dispensary, an' uthers to Doctor Gibb's,
An' sum sought out the Infirmary to mend their broken ribs.

 Chorus - *O lads, etc.*

Noo when we gat to Paradise thor wes bonny gam begun,
Thor wes fower-and-twenty on the bus, man, hoo they danced an'
    sung;
They called on me to sing a sang, aw sung them "Paddy Fagan."
Aw danced a jig an' swung me twig that day aw went to Blaydon.

Chorus - *O lads, etc.*

We flew across the Chain Bridge
    reet into Blaydon toon,
The bellman he was callin' there -
    they call him Jackey Brown,
Aw saw him talkin' to sum cheps,
    an' them he was pursuadin',
To gan an' see Geordy Ridley's show
    in the Mechanics' Hall at Blaydon.

Chorus - *O lads, etc.*

The rain it poor'd a' the day, an' myed the groon'd quite muddy,
Coffy Johnny had a white hat on - they war shootin', "Whe stole the
    cuddy?"
There was spice stalls an' munkey shows, an' aud wives selling
    ciders,
An' a chep wiv a happeny roondaboot shootin', "Noo, me boys, for
    riders".

Chorus - *O lads, ye shud a' seen us gannin, etc.*

HAWK'S MEN AT THE BATTLE OF WATERLOO.

MAN, aa fell in wi' Ned White the other day. Ye knaa Ned and other twenty-fower o' Haaks's cheps went out te the Peninsular War, where Wellin'ton was, ye knaa. Se, as we wor hevin' a gill tegithor, aa says te him, "Ned, d'ye mind when ye wor in the Peninsular War?" "Aa should think aa de," says he. "Did ye ever faall in wi' Wellin'ton?" says aa. "Wellin'ton!" says he; "wey, man, aa knaa'd him. Wey, just the day afore the Battle o' Waterloo he sent for me. 'Ned,' he says, 'tyek yor twenty- fower cheps,' he says, 'an gan up and shift them Frenchmen off the top o' yon hill.' 'Aal reet,' says aa, 'but it winnit tyek all the twenty-fower,' aa says. 'Ah, but it's Napolean's crack regiment,' he says, 'ye'd bettor tyek plenty.' 'Aal reet,' aa says, 'we'll suen shift them.' So doon aa cums te the lads, an' aa says, 'Noo ma lads, Wellin'ton wants us te shift yon Frenchmen off the top of yon hill.' 'Heor, Bob Scott, come here; hoo mony Frenchmen are ther up yondor?' 'Aboot fower hundred,' he says. 'Hoo mony on us will it tyek to shift them, Bob?' 'Oh, ten,' says Bob. 'Wey, we'll tyek four-teen,' aa says, 'just te humour the aad chap.' 'Aal reet,' they says. So off we set at the double alang the lonnen; but just as we turned the corner at the foot of the hill, whee should we meet but Bonnipart hees-sel on a lily-white horse, wiv a cocked hat on. 'Where are ye off te, Ned?' says he. 'Wey, te shift yon Frenchmen off yon hill!' 'Whaat!' he says, 'wey, that's ma crack regiment,' he says. 'Nivor mind that,' aa says, 'Wellin'ton says we hev te shift them, and shifted they'll be noo!' 'Get away, man, ye're coddin,' says he. 'Ne coddin' aboot it,' aa says; 'cum by!' 'Haud on, then,' he says; and he gallops reet up the hill on his lily-white horse, and shoots oot, 'Gan back, ma lads gan back! Heor's Ned White frae Haaks's and fourteen of his cheps comin' up te shift ye. Ye hevvent a happorth of chance!' Did aa ivvor see Wellin'ton? Wey, man, ye should think shyem."

J. A. STEPHENSON

THE WIFE'S REQUEST

A Newcastle man, troubled with a drunken wife, thought he would cure her of her bad habits by terror. When she was one day in a helpless state of intoxication he procured a coffin, placed her in it, and screwed the lid partially down. Waking up, but being unable to release herself, the wife demanded to know where she was. The husband informed her through the half- closed lid that she was in the regions of his Satanic Majesty. "And is thoo thor tee?" she asked. "Ay." "And hoo lang hes thoo been thor?" "Six months." "And hoo lang hev aa been thor?" "Three months." "Had away, then," said the thirsty wife, "and get's a gill o' whisky: thoo knaas the plyace bettor than aa de!"

SHIP AHOY !

A keelman was sent at dusk of evening in search of a ship. On arriving at the place where the craft lay among a fleet of other vessels, he felt somewhat abashed at discovering that he could not be positive as to the correctness of the name entrusted to his usually treacherous memory. Deeming it prudent, however, to make some attempt to attract the attention of the crew, he called out in his loudest tones, "Latitude, ahoy! Latitude, ahoy!" A roving tar, slightly inebriated, coming up at the time, in sailor fashion, said to the keelman, "Well, messmate, are you sure as how it ain't Longitude as you're a-wantinq?" "Wey," says the keelman, "aa divvent knaa but thoo's mebbies reet." Whilst rending the air with his cries for "Longitude ahoy," he was again brought to a stop upon hearing the sailor mutter, as he moved away, "Well I reckon that fellow knows no more about latitude or longitude than a shark knows about gratitude." "Gratitude!" cried the keelman, throwing the cap off his head: "wey, dash ma wig, man, that's the varry nyem aa want. Aa knaa'd it was the ootlandish nyem o'something wor owners didn't deal in!"

THE WHISTLOR

At a wedding party in the country, many years ago, the younger guests were contributing in turns to the harmony of the entertainment. On a young miner being pressed to sing, he bashfully declined. His sweetheart then tried to induce him to favour the company, and he at last exclaimed, "Leuks thoo, hinney, aa canna sing onny; but aa's as gude a whistlor as ivvor cocked a lip!"

6

"THROW DOWN THE BOTTLE"

A local comic singer of some repute, not only as a vocalist, but as a wit, was once admonished by a gentleman respecting a certain weakness to which he was addicted. "I am glad to hear, Edward," said the gentleman, "you have thrown away the bottle. I hope it's true." "It's quite true, sor," was the answer. "Aa did thraw'd away: but there wes nowt in't!"

THE DRUNKARD'S REPLY

A drunken character was accosted in the streets of Blyth one day by a person of evangelistic propensities, who found John in his usual condition. "Oh Jack," said he, "drunk again, aa see. Wey, man whaat'll become o' ye? Divvent ye knaa that drunkards cannot inherit the kingdom of heaven?" "Aye," says Jack, "aa knaa that; but aa divvent mean to get drunk when aa gans thor!"

THE POINTER DOG

A Northumberland miner had had a noted pointer dog, which was so perfect in his drill, and so unerring in his instincts for spotting game, that he sold it to a nobleman for a high price. The purchaser soon brought it back to Geordie, and told him it was a fraud. He said that it seemed to find game fast enough, but neither he nor his gamekeeper could either force it, or coax it, to lie down. The pitman observed, "It's varra queer that he should se syun hev forgettin' his mannors." Then he invited the nobleman to a test in his presence. They had not wandered far in the fields before the dog's nose 'pointed,' and it's tail poised like that of the Percy lion; then the gentleman shouted "Down, dog, down!" But the dog stood and moved not. "Didn't I tell you?" said the nobleman to the pitman. "Wey, man alive," said Geordie, "wad any dog understand language like that? Wait till aa tell him." Then in a low growling voice, like a he bear, he said, "Coil up, ye beggor!" The dog obeyed immediately.

A PLEASANT HOUSE

"De ye like yor new hoose?" asked a woman of her friend who had lately changed her place of residence. "Weel, it's not se pleasant as the other," was the reply, "caas aa could stand at the door and watch aall the funerals gan alang the chorchyaird!"

7

VULTURES

A party of Blyth men, including a philosopher from that quarter, were recently on a visit to North Sunderland, when a flock of birds flew overhead. "Bless me, what's them bords?" cried one of the excursionists. "Thor vultures," said a native. "Vultures," exclaimed the Blyth philosopher, "they flee heor, de they? Wey, they waak iboot wor plyace!"

LONG STOCKINGS

A miner entered a drapery establishment at Seaham Harbour one day. He was accosted by the master of the establishment as to what he could serve him with; the customer asked to see some "lang stockin's". After having had about a dozen pairs to inspect, he said that "nyen o' them wad de for him." "Well, how's that my good man? These are long enough." "That's all reet, mistor, but aa want a pair o' bow-legged yens!"

A PRECAUTION

At a village not far from Earsdon an old man died, and two women were called in to perform the last rites before burial. "Divvent tie his feet," one of the women was heard to exclaim, "or he'll not can waak through the gate when he gets te hiven!"

THE PLOUGHMAN'S BRAINS

A local farmer's daughter was somewhat annoyed by the attention of her father's ploughman, and she asked her parents to put a stop to his advances. The farmer found that his man was in the habit of hanging about the farmhouse at night awaiting an opportunity to speak to the young woman, and he determined to give him a fright. So he loaded an old blunderbuss with cold porridge, and the next night awaited the appearance of the love-sick son of toil. That worthy put in his appearance about the usual time, and on seeing him the farmer fired the blunderbuss full in his face. The plough-man fell to the ground in a terrible plight, full of the belief that his last hour had come. The noise brought out the farm hands, who went and raised him up. "Are ye much hort, man?" was the excited question. "Aa divvent knaa," he exclaimed, as he wiped the por-ridge from his beard; "but heor's ma brains aall ower ma hands an' fyece!"

A FRIEND OF PUBLICANS AND SINNERS

A local character in the neighbourhood of Jarrow, a great frequenter of public-houses, was accosted recently by a temperance friend who pointed out that he was despised and rejected by all respectable people, owing to his frequent visits to the public-house. "Ah, weel," was the reply, "if aa is despised and rejected by them, aa can easily see that it's for the syem reason that ma Lord and Master was despised and rejected - because aa's a friend of publicans and sinnors!"

A CYCLING NOVICE

A youth, residing in a suburb of Newcastle, was one day out for a ride on his bicycle. Being a bit of a novice at the pastime, he fell off his machine, as many learners are wont to do; and not having got into the way of mounting his iron steed, he was compelled to wheel it home. Whilst performing this necessary operation, the cyclist happened to pass a couple of workmen just returning from their day's labour, one of whom turned to the other and remarked, "Just tyekin' it oot for a waak, that's aall!"

Posh gent: After you with the match, my man.
Geordie: Efter me? Aa should think se. It's ma match!

Joe Wilson wrote a number of humourous tales which he recited along with his songs. The story of the man with the brown coat is probably based on a true incident which took place when Joe was an apprentice to Frank Robson the printer.

THE MAN WI' THE BROON TOP-COAT !

// IF thor's a man wiv a broon top-coat on calls, say aw's not in, Joe!" Them wes the varry words me maistor said to me one mornin aboot ten o'clock.

Me maistor wes one o' them sort o' cheps that cud spend a lang way faster then he cud myek't, an' as lang as he had it iv his hands he diddent care aboot pairtin wid te them that mebbies had mair reet tid nor him. In fact, he wes one o' them cheps that wad tyek all, an' nivvor dream o' payin owt if his creditors wad put up wid. Still he had a gud nyem amang his toon ackwentinces, - but bliss ye! whe hessent? - if they gan aboot treatin ivrybody. Thor's sum men 'ill myek ye beleeve yor sumbody else if ye'll only gie them a gill o' beer. So aw wassent astonish'd that mornin when me maister tell'd us te say he wassent in if a chep call'd wiv a broon top-coat on. Besides, aw knew thor wes a traveller (drest that varry way) had arrived i' the toon the day before, an' the gov'nor expected him, - tho he diddent want te see him, mind ye! So aw says, "A' reet, sor;" an' aw went on wi' me wark, hopin nebody wad cum, for aw wassent used wi' tellin a lee then, tho aw've had a bit of practice since. So aw sets me-sel agyen the window, as aw might see onybody that com doon the yard. Aw wad be there aboot half-an-oor when aw sees a tall, gud-lookin fellow, wiv a broon top-coat on, torn inte the entry an' myek tewards the shop.

10

"Here he is, maistor!" aw says; an' ye nivvor saw owt like the scene that follow'd. Thor wes ne chance o' getting away withoot bein seen, so me unfortunit imployer scrammils intiv a greet big cuppord there wes i' the room. But cuppords wes nivvor myed te haud men, or they wad had ne shelves in, so me noble gov'nor had te dubbil hi'sel up at the bottom, i' the kumpney ov a poke o' coals we had got the syem week. So aw locks the door, an' puts the key i' me pocket, an' myeks me-sel as cumfortable as aw cud under the sorkumstances.

"Is yor maistor in?" says tha man wi' the broon top-coat, as he open'd the door an' teuk a seat, as if he had been there afore - quite at hyem like.

"No!" aw says an' aw felt a' the blood i' me body rush te me fyece, eneuff te myek the man beleeve aw was tellin a lee, if he had teun ony notis on us. But no, he sat at his ease, luckin as if he had cum te leeve there, as happy as possible.

"Hoo lang will he be?" says he, as he drew a fob oot ov his pocket, an' started te fill his pipe, luckin roond for matches.

"Aw cannet say for an oor or two!" says aw, an' aw thowt that wad frighten him.

But no, there he sat, puffin away, an' watchin me at me wark, as if it wes a novelty te him.

"Oh," says he, "aw'm i' ne hurry; aw'm not tied for time, so aw think aw'll wait!"

Thor wes a crash i' the cuppord, as if thor wes sumthing rang, an' the man an' me luckt roond at the door, as if we expected it wad open.

"What's that?" he says, kind astonish'd

"Rats!" aw says; "wor awfully troubled wi' rats here!" an' aw felt as if he knew aw was tellin a whapper.

"Thor big uns, te myek a noise like that!" he said, as he sat doon agyen puffin away - an' there he sat for a full oor, tawkin tiv us aboot owt that com intiv his heed. But ivry noo an' then thor wes a stir i' the cuppord eneuff te let us knaw thor wes sumthin there alive, an' the man i' the broon top-coat appear'd te think se.

"Aw've cum frae Barry-Edge this mornin," says he, "te pay yor maister sum muney that aw've been awn him this three munths; aw wad come afore if aw haddent been se bizzy, but it cannet he help't - aw warn'd it i'll just be as ackseptabil noo!"

Just imadgin me feelins when he said this. But what wes mine te what me maistor's wad been? Here wes a man cum te pay muney, i'steed o' cravin for ony, an' the broon top-coat wes a' the cawse o' the fix we war in.

"Ye can tell yor maister aw call'd an'aw wad liked te heh seen him, as it's hard te tell when aw'll be i' the toon agyen!" says he.

"Ye'll mebbies meet him," says aw, an' aw thowt thor wes a chance, as the back door struck us.

"Gud-day!" says he.

"Gud-day!" says aw, an' me heart lowpt to me mooth when aw saw him gannin up the yard.

"Let's oot! let's oot, Joe!" groans a voice i' the cuppord, as if sumbody wes suffrin frae the teuth-ake.

"A' reet, sor," says aw, missin the key-hole an' puttin the key i' the rang way i' me hurry.

At last the pris'nor wes free, wiv a fyece ye wad swore had been up the chimley, an' dubbled up as if he had been born that way. Oot at the back door like a shot, an' inte the street, afore aw cud say nowt! Up aw runs te the heed o' the yard, te see the finish on't. An' there aw sees me maistor meet the man wi' the broon top-coat, shake hands wiv him se hearty, an' tyek him intiv a public hoose. Aw saw him ne mair that day!

Aboot an noor efter that *anuther* chep calls wiv a broon top-coat on - but it wes ne gud, me maistor wes oot this time for fairs!

12

A TOW FOR NOWT

A Tyneside Story

A well-known steamboat man named Forster, belonging to the Tyne, was about to proceed up the river to Newcastle from Jarrow in his tug-boat, when he was accosted by an impecunious keelman, who wanted a tow up to the Mushroom "for nowt". "Mr. Forster, hinney!" he shouted, "give us a tow, hinney; give us a tow up to the Mushroom, hinney!" "How do you know my name's Forster?" "Oh, aw knaw yor nyem's Forster, hinney. I've knawn ye awll yor life. I knew your fether afore ye. He was a canny chep, yor fether. He was particlar fond o' me, yor fether was. Give us a tow, hinney!" "Well, fling us yor rope." "There ye are, hinney. Yor the model o' yor fether, hinney; the model o' yor fether. Fling us off at the Mushroom, hinney! - at the Mushroom! Aye! yor the model o' yor fether." So Forster made the tow rope fast, and began to steam up the river. Now Forster was rather fond of a practical joke, and he thought it would be a good one not to fling the rope off at the Mushroom, but to tow him up to the bridge, about a mile higher up. So, on approaching the Mushroom, the keelman sang out, "Now, Mr. Forster, hinney, fling hor off, hinney, fling hor off." Forster took no notice. "Fling the rope off, hinney; fling the rope off. Here's the Mushroom!" Forster steered steadily on. "Fling the rope, Forster. Why, man, fling the rope off. Why! ye mun be a bad un. Ye are a bad un. Ye always war a bad un; and yor fether was a bad un afore ye."

J. A. STEPHENSON

Keep yor feet still

Wor Geordy and Bob Johnson byeth lay i' one bed
In a little lodgin' hoose that's doon the shore.
Before he'd been an hour asleep a kick from Geordy's fut
Made him waken up te roar i'steed o' snore.

Chorus:
Keep yor feet still Geordy Hinney
Let's be happy for the neet
For aw may nit be se happy thro' the day,
So give us that bit comfort keep yor feet still Geordy lad
And dinnet drive me bonny dreams away.

Aw dremt thor wes a dancin' held an'
    Mary Clark wes there
An' aw thowt we tript it leetly on the
    floor,
An' aw prest hor heevin' breest te mine
    when walsin' roon the room,
Thats mair than aw dor ivver de afore.

Ye knaa the lad she gans wi, they caall him Jimmy Green.
Aw thowt he tried te spoil us i' wor fun,
Buy aw dremt aw nailed 'im hevvy, an' blacked the big feul's eyes,
If aw'd slept its hard te tell what aw wad deun.

Aw thowt aw set hor hyem that neet;
    content we went alang,
Aw kissed hor lips a hundord times or
    mair,
An' aw wisht the road wad nivvor end,
    se happy like was aw,
Aw cud waak a thoosand miles wi'
    Mary there.

Aw dremt Jim Green had left the toon an' left his luv te me,
An' aw thowt the hoose wes fornished wi' the best.
An' aw dremt aw just had left the Chorch wi' Mary be me side,
When yor clumsy feet completely spoilt the rest.

HEH YE SEEN WOR JIMMY ?

OH, hinnies, what iver is aw gannin to de with that lad o' mine? His gawn to ha' maw life - aw's sure he is; it's wor Jimmy aw mean, ha' ye seen owt o' him? He's an awful lad. Wark! he'll work nyen. He's been gannin oot every day for the last six months te seek a job, and niver getten one yet - not likely while I keep him, he knaws better, hinney. Now, his fether wes a man, his fether was. If ye had only seen his fether cummin aalang the quayside iv a Sunday mornin wiv his white hat and his wooden leg, and a blue hankitcher round his neck; he was the varry spittin immige o' the Duke o' Wellington - umph-m, about the small o' the back, hinney. Oh dear me, when aw think o' his fether it reminds me of wor early days, when he used te cum sweetheartin me, in the springtime o' the year, when the cock robbin and the kitty wren and the moudy warp all joined together in a grand chorus o' delight - umph-m, it was lovely. He used to take me to Jesmond, down by the green water pool, him walkin on in front and me behint, an' aw didn't like that, ye knaw, and awwad say, "Give ower lettin me a-be," and then he put his airm round me waist, and, oh, such things he wad say tiv us! He once said 'at aw was varry like Mary Queen o' Scots - umph-m, about the back o' the neck, hinney! But he's deed and gyen now, hinney, and these lovely times is ower; but aw've still getten his wooden leg hinging aback o' the door as a mementer of the dear departed. Things is changed now, hinney. Aw heh te gan oot washing five days a week, eighteenpence a day an' me meat - little enough, aw think. If it wasent for a little drop o' gin aw get wi' a little drop of watter - not ower much watter, ye knaw, for it niver did agree with me - aw divent knaw what aw wad de.

Weel, hinney, whe de ye think aw seed the uther day? Aw was cummin doon the Groat Market, and aw just popped into Hell's Kitchen - aw beg yor pardin, hinney, but ye knaw where aw mean - where they keep the poker chain'd up for fear they knock one another on the heed wi'd, ye knaw; and aw'd just

gettin a half o' gin when whe should cum in but Hillar
Thompson - Geordy Thompson, ye knaw, but they call him
Hillar; he was brother te Billy Thompson - ye knawed Billy -
they byeth used te be wi' Billy Purvis, ye knaw. Hillar's just
aboot the height of six pennorth of copper, ye knaw, and always drunk - aw believe he was born drunk, aw niver saw
him sober i' maw life. He just gans aboot spootin' for beer -
spungin', ye knaw; so when he came in a chep says, "Let's hev
a recitation, Hillar." Why, that's just what he cum in for, de ye
see? so he gets on te the table and starts,

A chieftain to the highlands bound,

and then he stopped. "Aw knaw what he wants," says the
chep; "fetch him a quart o' beer, misses." And she did, and
Hillar slockened it off, hinney, ay, to the last gasp, and then he
started off afresh.

A chieftain to the highlands bound
Cried, boatman do not tarry,
An' I'll give thee a silver pound -

him give onybody a silver pund, he niver gov onybody a
copper fardin iv his life - niver! -

To row me o'er the ferry.
Oh, who is this wad cross Lochgyle,
This dark, this stormy water?
Oh, I'm the chief of Ulva's Isle, -

him the chief of Ulva's Isle! Why, his father and mother selled
apples and pears in Denton Chare -

And this Lord Ullin's daughter.
And fast before her father's men,
We two have fled together;
Oh, should they meet us in the glen,
My blood would stain the heather.

His blood stain the heather! Why, his blood was nowt but beer;
and just then, ye knaw, he stepped back on the table, te give a
bit elocution tiv his words - deye see? when he went reet ower
intiv a basket of eggs and biscuits belangin' tiv an au'd wife,
and myed a bonny smash. "Whe's gawn te pay for these?"
says the wife. "Haud yor gob," says Hillar; "aw'll eat them all
when we're deun."

From J. A. STEPHENSON'S Manuscript, 1891.

A DIFFICULT TASK
Customer: Can you take the grey hairs out of my moustache?
Barber (considering): Easier to tyek oot the black yens, sor!

CONSCIENCE MAKES COWARDS OF US ALL
Geordie was on his way one morning in May across a local cemetery to work. "Mar, Jack, this is grand growing morning for ye," he
remarked to a friend he met. "Wey, ivvorything is just springing
into life." Jack retorted, "Divven'd say that, Geordie, for gudness
sake; aa've got twe wives buried here".

AT THE CLUB CONCERT
Geordie stood up at the club concert: "How way oot," he said to his
mate, "aa've had eneuf o' this fal-de-dal."
Bill (sitting): "Sit doon, and divvent myek such a fyeul o' yorsel.
The consart'll be ower in a minute. Thor puttin' them on two's at a
time noo!"

A TOUGH CUSTOMER
One dark night, while a pitman was returning home to Seghill he
was stopped in a lonely part of the road by two strangers, who
demanded his money. Geordie made no reply, but at once attacked
his assailants. It was soon evident he was getting the best of it. One
of the thieves, however, seized a hedge-stake, and felled the pitman
to the ground. The robbers then rifled Geordie's pockets, but, find-
ing only sixpence, one of them remarked: "Begox, Jack, if the fond
beggor had had a shilling, he wad hev killed us byeth."

THE BOTTLE OF MEDICINE
Doctor (to Mrs. Black, whose husband had been ill): Well, Mrs.
Black, did your husband follow the directions on the bottle?
Mrs. Black: He'd hev broken his neck if he had.
Doctor: How is that?
Mrs. Black: Why he threw the bottle oot o' the window!

A THIRSTY CUSTOMER
"Let's hev a gill o' beer," said a customer at the Geordie Pride one
Saturday morning. "If aa'd knaan aa wes gan to be se dry the morn,
aa wad ha'e tyen an extra pint last neet!"

A SWELL OF TYNEMOUTH

A miner had come with his family for a happy day on the sands at Tynemouth. Approaching a boatman he asked: Hi, mistor, can we hev a sail oot?

Boatman: Cannot let ye hev a boat te-day.

Miner: Hoo's that then?

Boatman: Wey, thor's a swell on.

Miner: Swell, be hanged! Isn't wor money as good as his?

A CONFIDENT COMEDIAN

Angry club chairman: By God, Geordie, this tomfoolery will never do at all. Your audience has never clapped once.

Comedian: Clapped, my dear sir, clapped! Why, I've paralysed them. They can't clap!

DRY WORK

A farm labourer was busy digging drains in a field where a famous battle had once been fought.

A passing tourist: Well, my man, have you come across any relics of the great battle during your excavations?

Labourer: Why, sor, aa comes across aad boots, aad tins, aad bones and all kinds o' things, but aa nivvor comes across owt te sup!

AT THE DANCE

Geordie had been dancing vigorously with his girl for a long time.

Mary enquired: Is thoo het, Tommy?

Tommy: Het! Aa's bubbling ower wi' presspiration. Tell thoo what, Mary; aa'd see wore foreman blowed afore aa'd wark like this.

GEORDIE IN THE GRAVE

Grave-Digger (who has just finished digging a grave) to Geordie who had fallen in it when drunk: Hi, thor, what are ye deein' in ma grave?

Geordie (who had taken a short cut across the cemetery and fallen in): Your grave, be beggored! What aa want te knaa is, whaat are ye deein' oot on't?

The following two stories are by John Green of Sunderland (published 1897) and were supplied by Jack Armstrong.

THE SILK UMBRELLA

A Sunderland Shipwright took unto himself a wife, but alas! like the Moor of Venice, he "loved not wisely, but too well". The lady he saw fit to endow with his name and wordly goods was passing fair and truly virtuous - two estimable qualities in a woman; but to the sorrow and extreme regret of the husband, he found she either knew nothing of the duties of a housewife, or didn't care two straws about performing them. Poor Alick (his godfathers and godmothers had given him the name of Alexander) saw he had made a mistake before the honeymoon was half over; badly cooked victuals, a slovenly house, and an utter - nay, almost studied - neglect of his work-day apparel, induced him to the belief that, by the exercise of ordinary judgement, he might have done better.

One evening, after his tea, he dressed himself in his best, and before going out he said to the partner of his somewhat equivocal joys, "Jinny, aw'se gawn tiv the lodge to neet, an' while aw'se away aw wish thou wad set some buttons o' my fustain trousers; aw've telled ye about them till aw'se fairly tired, an' aw've had them tied up all day wi've pieces o' spunyarn. Now, Jinny, aw've myed my mind up, eff them buttons isn't on ti neet, aw'll gan ti wark iv the morning wi my best black suit;" and with this he marched out of the house in manifest wrath. Next morning his trousers were just in the same condition - not a button sewn on, not a stitch put in. Alick threw them from him with an oath, and proceeded leisurely to don his Sunday suit of superfine black, omitting nothing, from the patent leather boots to the "long-sleeved hat". After being thoroughly dressed he awoke his wife. "Now,

Jinny," he said, "aw tell'd ye what aw wad dee, an' aw intend ti di'd. What hev ye to say for yersel?" Jinny was probably something like the famous parrot, if she thought a great deal she said nothing; and Alick marched forth to his daily labour; but when half way down the stairs his steps were arrested by the sound of her voice. "Alick, come back!" "Ah, ah!" he ejaculated; "aw thowt this dodge wad fetch ye, awd lass; ye're coming tee, are ye?" He went back into the room with a triumphant smile on his face, a smile which would have becomingly illuminated the features of the Macedonian conqueror whose name he bore. "Now, then," he exclaimed, as he entered the room, "what d'ye want now, eh?" The wife of his bosom suffered her eyes to fall upon him for a single moment; then pointing languidly to one corner of the room, without so much as raising her head from the pillow, she said in a voice which, for even calmness and placidity, drove him almost to madness, "Alick, thou's forgettin' thy silk umbrella!"

AUNT TICKETTY

ONE fine morning in the month of June, a good many years ago, when the rising sun was darting his glad rays on the water, causing the placid bosom of Hendon bay to sparkle with golden light, a collier brig was seen approaching Sunderland harbour. The brig was under the charge of a well known pilot, who could handle her like a toy, and she was brought safely over the bar, and up as far as Hardcastle's slip, where she was moored to the buoys. While the vessel was being made fast with the hawser chains, the pilot was asked in the customary manner, by the skipper, to step into the cabin for the twofold purpose of receiving his pilotage money and refreshing his inner man with a drop of "something short."

Pocketing the fee, and lifting the glass to his lips with "Thank ye, sir, here's yer varry good hilth," the pilot proceeded to gaze with wrapt attention on an old-fashioned and curiously-made chair which stood in the cabin. After regarding it for some time with the deepest attention, he said, "That's a queer awd chair ye've gettin' thare, maister."

"Yes," replied the skipper; "that chair is about two hundred years old."

"Bliss us all! ye dinnot say see."

"Oh, yes," returned the captain, "it's quite a fact, I assure you. It's one of the Louis Quatorze pattern. I bought it in Hamburg especially on account of its *antiquity*."

"Indeed, sir," said the pilot, as he finished his glass, slightly mystified rather than enlightened by the captain's lucid explanation, and proceeded to quit the cabin, having been told to send down his partner, who was doing duty in the coble, to get a glass.

The invitation given by the pilot savoured more of pantomime than of words: it consisted of "Geodie," and an expressive jerk of the left thumb over the left shoulder in the direction of the cabin. This was as plain or plainer to "Geodie" than the most elaborately-worded invitation would have been, and he was up the side, along the deck, and into the cabin in a jiffy, while the pilot walked forward to see that the crew had made the hawser chain properly fast to the buoy. As he came aft again, he saw with marked astonishment his mate "Geodie" emerging from the cabin with the old-fashioned chair in his possession.

"Halloa!" the pilot exclaimed, "what are ye gawn ti' dee wi' that?"

"Aw'se gawn ti tak't tiv the maister's house."

"Where?"

"Ti the maister's house iv Dee Arcy Tarrace; he's gien us a shillin' for ti tak't up."

"Ye've meyd a mistake, Geodie; it hessn't ti gan tiv his house. Ye'd better ax him ageyn." "Nut mee," replied Geodie;

"he tell'd us plain enough, wiv his awn mouth."

"Vary weel, my man, " continued the pilot, sententiously, "dee yer awn way; but aw tell ye, ye'er wrang. He tell'd me quite a different story iv the cabin; he said he'd bowt it iv Hamburg, frev a chap they call Lewis Catall Patten, an' he gat it spesshally for his Aunt Ticketty; an' that's where it'll let te gan, ye'll see eff it hesn't."

● ● ● ● ● ● ● ● ● ● ● ● ● ● ● ● ● ●

THE PITMAN AND THE MAGISTRATE.

A pitman had to cross a railway every morning on his way to work. One morning he left the gate open, for which he was summoned to the police court. On being asked by the magistrate the reason he left the gate open, the pitman replied: "Wey, noo, luik heor, aa had buttor an' breed i' yen hand, an' ma hoggers i' t'other, an' ma picks ower ma back. Hoo could aa shut the gate, ye fond beggor?"

COMING DOWN STAIRS.

At a village not a score of miles from Bedlington, a miner, who lived in an upstairs flat, accidentally fell down stairs. His wife, hearing the noise, ran to the scene, and called out:—"O Jack, hes thoo faallen doon stairs?" "Oh," Jack replied, "it makes ne mettor; aa wes comin' doon onnway!"

A GENEROUS SPOUSE.

Jim and Geordy were talking about the good qualities of their respective wives. "Begox," said Geordy, "but wor Meg's a grand un. She's that kind, man, that if she only had half a loaf she'd give somebody else t'uthor half!"

A TEST OF MATRIMONY.

At a village in Durham, recently, two miners were heard in hot dispute on the knotty point whether a certain companion of theirs was married to the female who had the honour of sharing his bed and board. The following were the closing exchanges of the collo-quy : "Wey, Jack, man, aa tell thoo they're not married. Aa knaa nicely." "But they are, aa can tell thoo for a sartinty. Wey, man, didn't aa see him hoy a glass at her? Dis thoo think he'd de that if she warn't married?"

Boy: Hoo much are the black bullets, please?
Shopkeeper: Penny each, hinnie.
Boy: Hoo long will ye let's hev it in ma mooth for a ha'penny?

FROM THE SUBLIME TO THE RIDICULOUS

Not long ago, during stormy weather, a man and his wife went down to Tynemouth. They were watching the waves beat upon the shore, and the good man seemed to be impressed with the angry character of the scene. He was about to give vent to his feelings, when his wife, her eyes fixed on the sea, quietly remarked, "O Geordy! isn't it like soapsuds?"

A REMARKABLE VILLAGE

Whilst walking along a strange country lane, a gentleman came in contact with a pit lad, and accosted him thus: "Is there any village hereabouts, my fine fellow?" "Thor is, sor," responded the lad, "boot half a mile farthor alang the road." "And what might be the name of the village?" the gentleman further asked. "Aa divvent ken that, mistor; but thoo cannot varry weel misteck it, for thor's oney yen hoose!"

24

A STORY OF A PIG

A village not a hundred miles from Bellingham is blessed with a very zealous policeman, who on one occasion wished to find out the owners of some pigs that were occasionally allowed to stretch their legs on the village green. Meeting a youngster, he commenced: "D'ye keep a pig?" "Yes," was the reply. "Aa want to see't" says Robert. "Come on then," said the youngster, and, leading the way into the house, he pointed to the ceiling, saying, "Thor's yen half, and t'other yen's eaten!"

FRESH CRABS

Geordie: Is yor crabs fresh, mistor?
Fishmonger: Oh, aye, sor sartinly.
Geordie: Aall right, aa'll just try yen on wor Rover's tail.
Fishmonger (on seeing the dog running away with a crab hanging to its tail): Hi, mistor! caal back yor dog.
Geordie: Not aa. Ye mun caal back yor crab.

THE SOW AND THE THIRTEEN PIGS

A young Geordie farmer had occasion to call upon a neighbour with a message from his father. On his arrival he found the family, which was rather numerous, at dinner, and the young fellow, having stated his business, had then to answer the usual string of questions as to how they were all at home, how the crops were looking and so forth. The old farmer who, though well known to be wealthy, was also very stingy, omitted to ask his visitor to join them at table, so he sat talking till his fund of conversation was exhausted.

"Then ye hev nowt mair te tell us, Jack?" queried the old gentleman.
"Aa think not except it be that the aad soo's pigg'd," answered the young man.
"Hes't a good litter, then?" was the next question.
"Thorteen, but the warst on't is, she's only twelve tits."
"Aye," laughed the old farmer," what dis the thorteenth yen de then?"
"Oh! just whaat aa's deein' noo - sits ans leuks on!"

A PITMAN'S WIFE

The following conversation between two pitmen is said to have been heard, some years ago, in a train between Newcastle and Shields.

A: Eh! marraa, and hoo's thoo gitten on?

B: Wey, man, aa've been gitten married!

A: Married, He' ye? And what sort of a wife he'ye gitten?

B: Eh, man! She's a deevil.

A: A deevil, dis thoo say? Wey, man, but mine's warse than the deevil!

B: Warse than the deevil! Hoo dis thoo myek that oot?

A: Wey, dissent thoo read the Bible? Dissent it say, if thoo resists the deevil he'll flee fra thee? But if thoo resists wor Meg, by gox, she'll flee at thoo!

TIT FOR TAT

A little chimney sweep once entered a shop at Usworth Colliery and asked for a threepenny loaf of bread. The shopman handed him one. The boy looked at it, and said it was a "smaal yen". "Oh!" said the shopman, "it will be the less to carry." The lad then put two-pence-halfpenny on the counter, and then left. The shopman hastened to the door and shouted for him to come back, as he had not left enough money . "Oh!" said the lad, "it'll be the less to coont!"

AAD NICK'S SISTER

A woman resident in the neighbourhood of the Ouseburn was wishful to wean her husband from his habit of frequenting public-houses. She, therefore, persuaded her brother to act the part of a ghost, and frighten her husband on his way home. Accordingly, late the next night, he accosted the delinquent in a lonely part of the road. "Hoo are ye?" said the husband, "and whe are ye?" "Aa's Aad Nick," said the brother. "Oh!" was the reply, "gie us a wag o' yor han'. Aa'm, marriet te a sistor of yors!"

THE FISHWIFE'S ANSWER

A Cullercoats fishwife called on one of her customers. "Well, Mrs. Smith," the lady of the house asked, "and hows business today?" Mrs. Smith (the fishwife): "Why hinny, "aa's duen nowt this week an aa did twice as much last!"

LETTING THE LIGHT OUT

A young man employed as a engineer in Manchester came to Tyneside a short time ago on a visit to his friends, and went to see his old master, the village millwright. He was shown into the best parlour, which he found rather dark, having only one small window. Noticing a window in the room blocked up, he asked why they did not have that window opened out to which his old master replied: "Wey, Dick, lad, thoo elwis wes a fond beggor. Does thoo not knaa that that waall's due north? A window thor wad let the leet out!"

MAKING MONEY

In a public-house just outside Newcastle, a few weeks ago, a conversation took place between some men present as to a certain individual in the neighbourhood who had made a good sum of money, "nebody knaad hoo". Geordie Muffin was asked if he knew the man in question, and if he could account for so much money being "myed oot o' nowt". "Yis," answered Geordie, "aa kaad him varry weel. He was a queer man, an' could make money oot o' nowt. Aa knaa for a fact, myets, that he used te gan to Newcassel an' buy spades for haaf-a-croon, an' sell 'em for eighteen pence, and then myek a profit." There was a pause, when suddenly Geordie added, "Yis, 'caas the beggor nivvor paid for 'em!"

A STRANGER IN THE DISTRICT

Two men were walking in the neighbourhood of Lemington when the sun was setting in the west. A discussion arose between the two as to whether it was the sun or the moon. They determined to settle it by reference to an old woman that was coming towards them. Each stated his opinion, the one saying it was the sun, the other saying it was the moon. The old lady looked at the two in astonishment, and then said: "Aas sure aa dinnet knaa, hinnies; aa's a stranger in these pairts!"

POTATOES

Scene: A shop at Seaton Burn. Enter a miner's 'canny dowter' for half-a-stone of potatoes. Shopman: "They're a penny up, the potatoes, to-day." Canny Dowter: "Are they? Wey, then, let us hev a half-steyne of yestorday's!"

Cushie Butterfield

Aw's a broken-hearted keelman,
an' aw's owerheed in luv,
Wiv a yung lass in Gyetshed,
an aw calls her me duv;
Her nyem's Cushy Butterfield,
an' she sells yalla clay,
An' her cusin is a muckman,
an' they call him Tom Gray.

Chorus:
She's a big lass, an' a bonny one,
An' she likes her beer;
An' they call her Cushy Butterfield,
An' aw wish she was here.

Her eyes are like two holes in a blanket burnt throo,
An' her brows in a mornin wad spyen a young coo;
An' when aw heer her shootin "Will ye buy ony clay,"
Like a candy man's trumpet, it steels maw young hart away.

Chorus - *She's a big lass, an' a bonny one, etc.*

Ye'll oft see her doon at Sandgate
  when the fresh herrin cums in;
She's like a bagfull o' sawdust
  tied roon wiv a string;
She weers big golashes, te,
  an' her stockins was wonce white,
An' her bedgoon is a laelock,
  an' her hat's nivor strite.

Chorus - *She's a big lass an' a*
bonny one, etc.

When aw axed her te marry me, she started te laff,
"Noo, nyen o' yor munkey tricks, for aw like ne such chaff!"
Then she start'd a bubblin, an' she roar'd like a bull,
An, the cheps i' the keel says aw'm nowt but a fyeul.

Chorus - *She's a big lass, an' a bonny one, etc.*

She says, "The chep that gets me'll
  heh te work ivry day,
An' when he cums hyem at neets
  he'll heh te gan an' seek clay;
An' when he's away seekin't
  aw'll myek balls an' sing,
'Weel may the keel row
  that maw laddie's in!'"

  Chorus - *She's a big lass, an' a bonny*
  one, etc.

Noo, aw heer she hes anuther chep, an' he hews at Shipcote,
If aw thowt she wad deceeve me, aw'd sure cut me throat;
Aw'll doon the river sailin, an' sing 'Aw'm afloat',
Biddin adoo te Cush Butterfield an' the chep at Shipcote.

Chorus - *She's a big lass, an' a bonny one, etc.*

THE
LONG PACK
A Northumbrian Tale

I T WAS in the year 1723, when Colonel Ridley returned from India, with what, in those days, was counted an immense fortune, and retired to a country seat on the banks of North Tyne, in Northumberland. The house was rebuilt, and furnished with every thing elegant and costly; and amongst others, a service of plate supposed to be worth £1000. He went annually to London with his family, during the winter months of the year, and at these times there were but few domestics left in his house. At the time treated of, the only domestics remaining were, a servant maid, of the name of Alice, who kept the house, and two men, who threshed the corn, and took care of the cattle and out-buildings.

One afternoon as Alice was sitting spinning some yarn for a pair of stockings for herself, a pedlar entered the hall with a comical pack on his back. Alice had seen as long pack and as broad a pack; but a pack equally as long, broad, and thick, she declared she never saw. It was about the middle of winter, when the days were short, and the nights cold, long and wearisome. The pedlar was a handsome, well-dressed man, and very likely to be an agreeable companion for such a maid as Alice, on such a night as that; yet Alice declared, that from the very beginning she did not like him greatly; and though he introduced himself with a little ribaldry, and a great deal of flattery interlarded, yet when he came to ask a night's lodging, he met with a peremptory refusal; he jested on the subject, said he believed she was in the right, for that it would be impossible for him to keep his own bed, and such a sweet creature lying alone under the same roof - took her on his knee and a ravished a kiss. But all would not do. No, she would not consent to his staying there. "But are you really going to put me away to-night?" "Yes." "Indeed, my dear girl, you must not be so unreasonable; I have come straight from Newcastle, where I have been purchasing a fresh stock of goods, which are so heavy that I cannot travel far with them; and as the people around are all of the poorer sort, I will rather make you a present of the greatest shawl in my pack before I go further." At the mentioning of the shawl, the picture of deliberation was

portrayed in lively colours in Alice's face for a little; but her prudence overcame. "No, she was but a servant, and had orders to harbour no person about the house but such as came on business, nor they either, unless well acquainted with them." "What the worse can either your master, or you, or any other person, be, of suffering me to tarry until the morning." "I entreat you not to insist, for here you cannot be." "But, indeed, I am not able to carry my goods further to-night." "Then you must leave them, or get a horse to carry them away." "Of all the inflexible beings I ever saw, thou are the first! But I cannot blame you, your resolution is just and right. Well, well, since no better may be, I must leave them, and go search for lodging myself somewhere else, for, fatigued as I am, it is as much as my life is worth to endeavour carrying them further." Alice was rather taken at her word; she wanted nothing to do with his goods: the man was displeased at her, and might accuse her of stealing some of them; but it was an alternative she had proposed, and against which she could start no plausible objection, so she rather reluctantly consented. "But the pack will be better out of your way," said he, "and safer, if you will be so kind as lock it by some room or closet." She then led him into a low parlour, where he placed it carefully on two chairs, and went his way, wishing Alice a good night.

When Alice and the pack were left in the large house by themselves, she could not, for her life, quit thinking of the pack one moment. What was in it which made it so heavy that its owner could not carry it? She would go and see what was in it. It was a very curious pack. At least she would go and handle it, and see what she thought was in it. She went into the parlour - opened a wall-press: she wanted nothing in the press: she never so much as looked into it; her eyes were fixed on the pack. "It was a very queer pack - it was square the one way, but not square the other way - it was a monstrous queer pack." It was now wearing late. She returned from the room in a sort of trepidation - sat down to her wheel, but could not spin one thread.

What surmises will fear not give rise to in the mind of a woman? She lighted a candle and went into the parlour, closed the window shutter, and barred them; but before she came out, she set herself upright, held in her breath, and took another steady and scrutinizing look of the pack. God of mercy! She saw it moving visibly as ever she saw anything in her life Every hair in her head stood upright. Every inch of flesh on her body crept like a nest of pismires [ants]. She hastened into the kitchen as fast as she could for her knees bent under the load of terror that had overwhelmed the heart of poor Alice. She puffed out the candle, lighted it again, and, not being able to find a candlestick, though a dozen stood on the shelf in the fore kitchen, she set it in a water-jug, and ran out to the barn for old

Richard. "Oh, Richard! Oh, for mercy, Richard, make haste, and come into the house. Come away, Richard." "Why, what is the matter, Alice? What is wrong?" "Oh, Richard, a pedlar came in the hall, entreating for lodging. Well, I would not let him stay on any account, and behold he is gone off and left his pack." "And what is the great matter in that?" said Richard, "I will wager a penny he will look after it before it shall look after him." "But, oh, Richard, I tremble to tell you! We are all gone, for it is a living pack." "A living pack!" said Richard, starting at Alice, and letting his chops fall down. Richard had just lifted the flail over his head to begin threshing a sheaf; but when he heard of a living pack, he dropped one end of the hand-staff to the floor, and, leaning on the other, took such a look at Alice. He knew long before that Alice was beautiful, he knew that ten years before, but he never took such a look at her in his life. "A living pack?" said Richard. "Why the woman is mad without all doubts." "Oh, Richard! come away. Heaven knows what is in it; but I saw it moving as plainly as I see you at present. Make haste and come away, Richard." Richard did not stand and expostulate any longer, nor even to put on his coat, but followed Alice into the house, assuring her by the way, that it was nothing but a whim, and of a piece with many of her fantasies. "But," added he, "of all the foolish ideas that ever possessed my brain, this is the most infeasible. How can a pack of napkins and muslins, and corduroy breeches, perhaps, ever become alive? It is even worse than to suppose a horse's hair will turn an eel. "So saying, he lifted the candle out of the jug, and turning round, never stopped till he had his hand upon the pack. He felt the bales that surrounded its edges to prevent the goods being rumpled and spoiled, by carrying the cords that bound it, and the canvass in which it was wrapped. "The pack was well enough. He found nought about it that other packs wanted. It was just like other packs made up of the same stuff. And a good large pack it was. It would cost the honest man £20 if not more. It would cost him more; but he would make it all up again, by cheating fools, like Alice, with his baubles." Alice testified some little disappointment at seeing Richard unconvinced, even by ocular proof. She wished she had never seen either him or it, howsoever, for she was convinced there was something mysterious about it, that they were stolen goods, or something that way; and she was terrified to stay in the house with it. But Richard assured her the pack was right enough.

During this conversation, in came Edward, a lad about 16 years of age, who herded the cattle. He was son to a coal-driver on the border, and possessed a good deal of humour and ingenuity, but somewhat roguish, forward, and commonly very ragged in his apparel. He was at this time wholly intent on shooting the crows and birds that alighted in whole flocks where he foddered the cattle. He had bought a huge old military gun, which he denominated Copenhagen, and was continually thundering away at them. He seldom killed any, if ever, but he once or twice knocked off a few feathers, and after much narrow inspection, discovered some drops of blood on the snow. He had at this very moment come in a great haste for Copenhagen, having seen a glorious chance of sparrows, and a robin-red-breast among them, feeding on the site of a corn rick, but hearing then talk of something mysterious, and a living pack, he pricked up his ears, and became all attentive. "Faith, Alice," said he, "if you will let me, I'll shoot it." "Hold your peace, fool," said Richard. Edward took the candle from Richard, who still held it in his hand, and gliding down the passage, edged open the parlour door, and watched the pack attentively for about two minutes. He came back with a spring, and with looks very different from those which regulated his features as he went down. As sure as he had death to meet with he saw it stirring. "Hold your peace, you fool," said Richard. Edward swore again that he saw it stirring; but whether he really thought so, or he only said so, is hard to determine. "Faith, Alice," said he again, "if you will let me, I'll shoot it." "I tell you to hold your peace, you fool," said Richard. "No," said Edward, "in the multitude of counsellors there is safety; and I will maintain this to be our safest plan. Our master's house is confided to our care, and the wealth that it contains may tempt some people to use stratagems. Now, if we open up this man's pack, he may pursue us for damages to any amount; but if I shoot at it, what amends can he get of me? If there is anything that should not be there, Lord, how I will pepper it; and if it is lawful goods, he can only make me pay for the few that are damaged, which I will get at valuation; so, if none of you will acquiesce, I will take all the blame myself, and aim a shot at it." Richard said, whatever was the consequence, he would be blameless. A half delirious smile rather distorted than beautified Alice's pretty face; but Edward took it for an assent to what he had been advancing, so snatching up Copenhagen he hasted down the passage, and, without hesitating a moment, fired at the pack. Gracious God! the blood gushed out upon the floor like a torrent, and a hideous roar, followed by the groans of death, issued from the pack. Edward dropped Copenhagen upon the ground, and ran into the kitchen like one distracted. The kitchen was darkish, for he had left the candle in the parlour; so taking to the door, without being able to utter a word, he ran to the hills like a wild roe,

looking over each shoulder as fast as he could turn his head from the one to the other. Alice followed as fast as she could, but lost half the way of Edward. She was all the way sighing and crying most pitifully. Old Richard stood for a short for a short space rather in a state of petrification, but at length, after some hasty prayers, he went into the parlour. The floor was covered with blood, and the pack thrown upon the ground; but the groans and cries were ceased, and only a kind of guttural noise was heard from it. Knowing that then something must be done, he ran after his companions and called on them to come back. Though Edward had escaped a good way, and was still persevering on, yet, as he never took long time to consider the utility of any thing, but acted from immediate impulse, he turned and came as fast back as he had gone away. Alice also came homeward, but more slowly, and crying even more bitterly than before. Edward overtook her, and was holding on his course, but, as he passed, she turned away her face, and called him a murderer. At the sound of this epithet, Edward made a dead pause, and looked at Alice with a face much longer than it used to be. He drew in his breath twice, as if going to speak; but he only swallowed his spittle, and held his peace.

They were soon all three in the parlour, and, in no little terror or agitation of mind, loosed the pack, the principal commodity of which was a stout young man, whom Edward had shot through the heart. To paint the feelings, or even the appearance of young Edward, during this scene, is impossible: he acted little, spoke less, and appeared in a hopeless stupor: the most of his employment consisted in swallowing his spittle, and staring at his two companions.

It is most generally believed, that when Edward fired at the pack, he had not the most distant idea of shooting a man; but seeing Alice so jealous of it, he thought the Colonel would approve of his intrepidity, and protect him from being wronged by the pedlar; and besides he had never got the chance of a shot at such a large thing in his life, and was curious to see how many folds of the pedlar's fine haberdashery ware Copenhagen would drive the drops through, so that when the stream of blood burst from the pack, accompanied with the dying groans of a human being, Edward was certainly taken by surprise, and quite confounded; he indeed asserted, as long as he lived, that he saw something stirring in the pack, but his eagerness to shoot, and his terror on seeing what was done, which was no more than what he might have expected, had he been certain he saw the pack moving, makes this assertion rather doubtful. They made all possible expedition in extracting him, intending to call in medical assistance, but it was too late; the vital spark was gone, for ever. "Alas!" said old Richard, heaving a deep sigh, poor man, 'tis all over with him I wish he had lived a little longer to have repented of this, for he has surely died in a bad cause. Poor man! he was somebody's son, and, no doubt, dear to them, and nobody can tell how small a crime this hath, by a regular gradation, become the fruits of."

The way that he was packed up was awful and curious. His knees were brought up parallel to his navel, and his feet and legs stuffed in a hat-box; another hat-box, a size larger, and wanting the bottom, made up the vacancy betwixt his face and knees, and there being only one fold of canvas around this, he breathed with the greatest freedom; but it had undoubtedly been the heaving of his breast which had caused the movement noticed by the servants. His right arm was within the box, and to his hand was tied a cutlass, with which he could rip himself from his confinement at one. There were also four loaded pistols secreted with him, and a silver wind-call. On coming to the pistols and cutlass, "Villain," said old Richard, "see what he has here. But I should not call him a villain," said he again, softening his tone, "for he is now gone to answer at that bar where no false witness, nor loquacious orator, can bias the justice of the sentence pronounced on him. We can judge only from appearances, but thanks to our kind Maker that he was discovered, else it is probable that none of us would have seen the light of a new day." These moral reflections from the mouth of old Richard, by degrees raised the spirits of Edward; he was bewildered in uncertainty, and had undoubtedly given himself up for lost; but he now began to discover that he had done a meritorious and manful action, and, for the first time since he had fired the fatal shot, ventured to speak. "Faith, it was lucky that I shot," said Edward; but none of his companions answered either good or bad. Alice, though rather grown desperate, behaved and assisted better at this bloody affair than might have been expected. Edward surveyed the pistols all around, two of which were of curious workmanship. "But what do you think he was going to do with all these?" said Edward. "I think you need not ask that," Richard answered. "Faith, it was a mercy that I shot, after all," said Edward, "for if we had loosed him out, we would have been all dead in a minute. I have given him a devil of a broadside, though. But look ye, Richard, providence has directed me to the right spot, for I might as readily have lodged the contents of Copenhagen in one of these empty boxes." "It has been a deep laid scheme," said Richard, "to murder us and rob our master's house; there must certainly be more concerned in it than these two."

Ideas beget ideas often quite different, and then others again in unspeakable gradation, which run through, and shift in the mind with as much ease and velocity as the streamers round the pole in a frosty night. On Richard's mentioning more concerned, Edward instantaneously thought of a gang of thieves by night. What devastation he would work amongst them with Copenhagen: how he would make some to lie with their guts in their arms, blow the nether jaws from one, and scatter the brains of another: how Alice would scream, and Richard would pray, and every thing would go on like the work of a wind-mill. Oh, if he had nothing to do but shoot, but the long time he always lost in loading, would subject him to a triple disadvantage in the battle. This immediately suggested the necessity of having assistance, two or three others to shoot and keep them at bay while he was loading. The impulse of the moment was Edward's monitor. Off he ran like fire, and warned a few of the Colonel's retainers, who he knew kept guns about them; these again warned others, and at eight o'clock they had 25 men in the house, and 16 loaded pieces, including Copenhagen, and the four pistols found on the deceased. Theses were distributed amongst the front windows in the upper stories, and the rest, armed with pitch forks, old swords, and cudgels, kept watch below. Edward had taken care to place himself, with a comrade, at a window immediately facing the approach to the house, and now, backed as he went by such a strong party, grew quite impatient for another chance. All, however, remained quiet until and hour past midnight, when it entered into his teeming brain to blow the thief's silver wind- call, so, without warning any of the rest, he set himself out at the window, and blew until all the hills and woods around yelled their echoes. This alarmed the guards, as not knowing the meaning of it; but how they were astonished at hearing it answered by another at no great distance.

The state of anxiety into which this sudden and unforeseen circumstance threw our armed peasants, is more easily conceived than described. Every breast heaved quicker, every breath was cut and flustered by the palpitations of an adjoining heart, every gun was cocked, and pointed towards the court gate, every orb of vision was trained to discover the approaching foe, by the dim light of the starry canopy, and every ear expanded to catch the distant sounds as they floated on the flow frosty breeze.

The suspense was not of long continuance. In less than five minutes the trampling of horses was heard, which increased, as they approached, to the noise of thunder, and, in due course, a body of men on horseback, according to their account, exceeding their number, came up at a brisk trot, and began to enter the court gate. Edward, unable to restrain himself any longer, fired Copenhagen in their faces; one of the foremost dropped, and his horse made a spring toward the hall door. This discharge was rather premature, as the wall still shielded a part of the gang from the bulk of the windows; it was, however, the watch-word of all the rest, and, in the course of two seconds, the whole 16 guns were discharged at them. Before the smoke dispersed, they were all fled like fire, no doubt greatly amazed at the reception which they got. Edward and his comrades ran down stairs to see how matters stood, for it was their opinion that they had shot them every one, and that their horses had taken fright at the noise, and galloped off without them; but those below warmly protested against opening any of the doors until day, so they were obliged to betake themselves again to their places upstairs.

Though our peasants had gathered up a little courage and confidence in themselves, their situation was curious, and to them a dreadful one: they saw and heard a part of their fellow creatures moaning and expiring in agonies in the open air, which was intensely cold, yet durst not go to administer the least relief, for fear of a great surprise. An hour or two after the great brush, Edward and his messmate descended again, and begged hard for leave to go and reconnoitre for a few minutes, which, after some disputes, was granted. They found only four men fallen, which

38

appeared to them to be all quite dead. One of them was lying within the porch. "Faith," said Edward, "here's the gentleman I shot." The other three were without, at a considerable distance from each other. They durst not follow their track farther, as the road entered betwixt groves of trees, but retreated into their posts without touching anything.

About an hour before day, some of them were alarmed at hearing the sound of horses' feet a second time, which, however, was only indistinct, and heard at considerable intervals, and nothing of them ever happened. Not long after this, Edward and his friend were almost frightened out of their wits, at seeing, as they thought, the dead man within side the gate, endeavouring to get up and escape. They had seen him dead, lying surrounded by a deluge of congealed blood, and nothing but the ideas of ghosts and hobgoblins entered their brains; they were so indiscreet as never to think of firing, but ran and told the tale of horror to some of their neighbours. The sky by this time grown so dark, that nothing could be seen with precision, and they all remained in anxious incertitude, until the opening day discovered to them, by degrees, that the corpses were all removed, and nothing left but large sheets of frozen blood; and that the morning's alarms, by the ghost and the noise of horses, had been occasioned by some of the friends of the men that had fallen, conveying them away for fear of a discovery.

Next morning the news flew like fire, and the three servants were much incommoded by crowds of idle and officious people that gathered about the house, some enquiring after the smallest particulars, some begging to see the body that lay in the parlour, and others pleased themselves with poring over the sheets of crimson ice, and tracing the drops of blood on the road down the wood. The Colonel had no country factor, nor any particular friend in the neighbourhood, so the affair was not pursued with that speed which was requisite to the discovery of the accomplices, which, if it had, would have been productive of some very unpleasant circumstances, by involving sundry respectable families, as it afterwards appeared but too evident. Dr. Herbert, the physician, who attended the family occasionally, wrote to the Colonel, by post, concerning the affair, but, though he lost no time, it was some days before he arrived. Then indeed, advertisements were issued, and posted up in all public places, offering rewards for a discovery of any person killed or wounded of late. All the dead and sick within twenty miles were inspected by medical men, and a most extensive search made, but all to no purpose. It was too late; all was secured. Some indeed were missing, but plausible pretences being made for their absence, nothing could be done: but certain it was, sundry of these were never more seen or heard of in the country, although many of the neighbourhood declared they were such people as nobody could suspect.

The body of the unfortunate man who was shot in the pack lay open for inspection a fortnight, but none would ever acknowledge so much as having seen him. The Colonel then caused him to be buried at Bellingham; but it was confidently reported that his grave was opened, and his corpse taken away. In short, no one concerned in this base and bold attempt was ever discovered. A constant watch was kept by night for some time. The Colonel rewarded the defenders of his house liberally. Old Richard remained in the family during the rest of his life, and had a good salary for only saying prayers amongst the servants every night. Alice was married to a tobacconist at Hexham, and Edward was made the Colonel's gamekeeper, and had a present of a find gold mounted gun given him.